A Pocket Full of Poetry

by Kailey Giles

D0710946

Dedicated to all of my supportive friends and teachers. To my magnificent dad, mom, brother, and sister for always being there for me, even when it wasn't about the book. Especially to my eldest sister Sadie for being my example of independence, strength, and a true poet.

Mother Nature

Her breathing is the wind,

Her eyes are the pools or the deep blue sea,

Her face is a clear perfect valley,

Her hands are gentle flowers,

Her mind is the roar of a lion,

Her smile is the brightness of the sun,

Her anger is the volcano erupting,

Her tears are the raindrops slipping to the earth,

The stars are the signs of her million wonders.

Flowers

I love to smell flowers

They smell so sweet,

Every flower type is so neat,

I love to see roses when they're red,

I want lilies in my flower bed.

I like to feel petals they feel so soft.

I wouldn't want enough flowers to fill a loft,

But one or two would be okay,

And when I get married I'll want a bouquet!

The Colored Flowers

A rose

Red as scarlet.

A violet

With an aroma as sweet as chocolate.

A daisy

Bright but calm

A sunflower

With petals blossoming out farther than a
grown man's palm.

A lily

Springing up to the stars.

A tulip

Growing so perfectly as to have no scars.

Red Rose, Green Leaves

A single red speck,

Floating on a sea of endless green,

Luxurious petals pulling outward while sitting atop

Long green fingers.

Long green fingers that were holding it up to the moon,

Allowing it to drink in the moonlight and stardust.

Yet just a rose it's a magnificent thing,

Sitting on plain but perfect leaves.

Leaves

Leaves.

What a marvelous thing,

Magnificent,

Miraculous,

Marvelous thing.

Knowing when to change colors and when to fall.

Knowing when to sprout out in delicious green,

And when to shrivel.

Leaves grow on,

And change through the seasons,

But please don't ever change.

The Scenery

The vibrant blue sky,

The dancing green grass,

The chirping black crows,

The waving brown branches,

The soft yellow flowers,

And the delicate rainbow butterfly wings

Painted a perfect scenery.

Swan Lake

The lake is brimming with shinning waters,

The air is twinkling with sparkling magic,

The pine trees are lustrous with thin green needles,

The ground dances with green whiskers,

And in the midst of all this beauty

Gliding through the water, is a magnificent creature

With a twinkling white coat of feathers

A swan elegantly swims around the lake.

The Window

I look out the window every day,

And sometimes I see the smaller children play.

Through the window

I see the sun rise,

Through the window

I watch as the morning dew dries,

Through the window

I see the valley clear,

Through the window

I hear a song bird near,

Through the window I see the stars bright,

As I look out the window,

I whisper good night.

The Sky

The sky is a miracle,

A marvelous thing

From its stars up above

To its storms down below

It bestows the snow, rain, and sleet

It provides the sun, moon, and stars

It cannot be for tolled,

Of what it will bring.

Sun Set

As the sun went down

The daylight melted,

And the vibrant colors perfectly molded,

And in my mind a great canvas so white,

My mind was ready,

To paint a wondrous sight.

Sun

First it starts at the Earth's thin line,

And then soars up into the sky,

And there it gives its rays of heat,

That fall to the earth ware they always meet,

The children who are outside to play,

That enjoy those heat waves every day.

Now the sun must descend,

Into the Earths horizon ware it will begin again.

Walking in a Cloud

The cloud was here all around,

But not in the sky on the ground,

The cloud was misty you could not see,

It set a haze on the flowers that was oh so pretty,

Then my situation accrued to me then,

I was walking in a cloud sent from heaven.

Clouds Alit

A wondrous sight

For the imagining eyes

The sun sinking down into a sun rise

Shedding its rays upon the clouds

Setting them alit in many shades,

Of red, orange and yellow blaze.

The Storm

Tap, Tap, Tap, Tap,

The steady beat of the rain.

Flash, Flash, Flash, Flash,

The streaks of lightning through the clouds.

Boom, Boom, Boom, Boom,

The heavy roar from the mighty thunder.

Tap, Flash, Boom, Bang,

Here comes a storm on its way.

Weeping Willow

Weeping willow,

With branches out vast,
tear leaves sliding,

To the grass.

A thick trunk

Sitting stilly

While stringy branches

Weep quietly.

Branches like Arms

Trees are like people,

They need nurturance,

They need air,

But most importantly, their branches are like arms.

Arms that are always lifted

Looking as if they're welcoming you to a hug,

Trees seem friendly,

,

Now think of this,

All the trees in the world

If they were alive

The world would be nearly perfect.

If we really tried

We could make the same world.

Lift your arms

Be friendly,

Be welcoming,

Live as the trees.

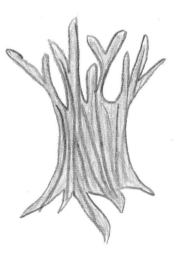

Spring

Flowers blossoming,

Butterflies flying,

People picnicking,

And people camping.

Winter is over,

But spring is just beginning.

Summer

Watermelon slices,

Sunshine rays,

Bathing suits,

Sprinkler sprays.

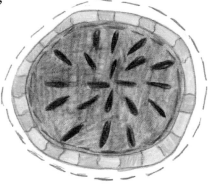

Cooling shorts,

Sunshine tans,

Vacations to the beach,

And hours in front of fans.

Raining sunshine,

Raining heat,

Summer is the season

The seasons try to beat.

Fall

As the crisp leaves fall it is a wonderous sign,

For a new season is upon us all.

The days start to shorten

As the nights start to lengthen,

And the house starts to be filled

With the sweet aroma of ginger and pumpkin.

As Thanksgiving draws nearer

And the pumpkins start to grow,

The cool fall air

Has an orange sweet glow.

Winter

The now quiet sun

Tried to melt the still ice,

But to his dismay,

His price did not pay,

As the ice never seemed to melt away.

Winter Times

The cozy coat

Was pulled tight.

The hat and mittens,

Snug in their positions.

The boots all fluffy

To keep the feet snugly,

And the gloved hands in the pocket

To protect them from the cold.

The cool fresh air,

Nipped the skin.

The light breath wafted to the sky.

The cheeks turning rosy pink.

The toes freezing solid,

And the fingers even now,

 Tingling from the cold.

Ember

A single ember

Flew on the wind

Away from mother fire

Free to fly,

And free to overcome its horrific fate.

The fate of being swallowed up

By a dark, lifeless, ash,

But the ember flew on and kept its light,

 Burning bright.

Misties

Twinkling snowflakes,

Falling to a sea of snow.

Moon milk glaze,

Glazing the spherical earth.

A Light Line,

A silver line.

A shiny thread.

A light with life,

Not filled with dread.

So precious,

So special,

So magical,

And bright

Encircle me

And protect me

As I sleep this starry night.

Truly Seeing

The true beauty of a person,

Can't be seen with your eyes,

But detected by your heart.

Determination

Our determination should run like water,

When faced by an obstacle,

Water always finds a way around it,

Whether it's over, under or simply around.

We all have it in us to overcome our difficulties,

The only reason why we wouldn't is if we didn't believe we could.

The Past

People say the past is in the past.

Sometimes they say it doesn't matter,

They say the past is full of mistakes

And it is,

But how can you forget and let go of something

That is the foundation of who you are?

Miracles

When you blink,

You use muscles.

When you reach to grab something,

You use muscles.

When you walk to your room,

You use muscles

You do all of this,

Without having to tell yourself when you want it to happen

Just think of that

We are all wonderfully made miracles

Just waiting to make a difference

In the world.

Perfect

Her eyes stealing the stars,

To twinkle and shine.

Her lips draining color from strawberries

To be a soothing red.

Her skin sucking pollen

To be colored and sweet.

Her hair sipping the midnight sky

To be a magnificent black.

Her perfect state

Her perfect self.

The Stony

The sunlight transformed her hair gold,

The wind blew away her worries,

The sweet scent of flower dotted fields cleansed out her soul,

The ocean waves washed out her thoughts,

The still quietness turned her to stone.

Who I Am

My body is grounded to the Earth as a lions

Yet my heart is as free as a bird that soars.

I am as a delicate flower,

Yet my thought and mind are as a roar.

About the Author

Kailey Giles is a very dedicated, hardworking and creative 11-year-old. Over the past few years, she has gained a fondness for reading which has grown into a love for writing, especially poetry. She gathers her inspiration from her faith, family and from the wonders around her. As a military child, she feels blessed that she has been able to see and explore many wonders in diverse parts of the world, by having the opportunity to live in three different countries. Kailey hopes that her writing will help others to see the world through different eyes.

A Pocket Full of Poetry
Kailey Giles
Ms. Anderson's Publishing Club
Arnn Elementary School 2018-19

Made in the USA
Las Vegas, NV
22 January 2021

16356304R00026